Toddler Treasury

Illustrated by Katie Saunders

What Do You Think?

Are the girls:
- dancing
- running
- jumping

Is this cat:
- eating
- running
- sleeping

Is the boy:
- throwing
- climbing
- running

Is the girl:
- running
- skipping
- clapping

Are the children:
- playing
- dancing
- painting

Is the boy:
- throwing the ball
- catching the ball
- kicking the ball

Do You Know?

Which vehicle is red?

Who lays eggs?

 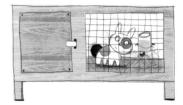

Who hops?

Who has a baby lamb?

Which vehicle you would find on a farm?

Who says "Moo"?

Toddler Quiz

You use this to brush your teeth.

 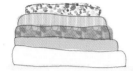

You keep your clothes in here.

You drink from this.

You sit on this.

You wear these in the rain

This is used for washing clothes.

Can You Remember?

Who owns this basket?
- Goldilocks
- Little Red Riding Hood
- Cinderella

Who eats this for breakfast?
- the Giant
- Cinderella's step-sisters
- The Three Bears

Who sat on a chair and broke it?
- Cinderella
- the Giant
- Goldilocks

Who lived in a house of straw?
- Jack
- Baby Bear
- a little pig

Who sold the cow for a bag of beans?
- the wolf
- Jack
- Daddy Bear

Who says:
- "Fee, Fi, Fo, Fum!"
- "I'll huff and I'll puff!"
- "Who's been sitting on my chair?"

When the Three Bears returned home they were surprised at what they found.

"Someone's been eating my porridge," growled Daddy Bear. And Mummy Bear added, "Someone's been eating my porridge too."

"Someone's been eating my porridge and has finished the bowl!" cried Baby Bear.

As he went to sit down, Daddy Bear growled, "Someone's been sitting in my chair!"

"And someone's been sitting in my chair too!" said Mummy Bear. Then Baby Bear cried, "Someone's been sitting in my chair and now it's broken."

The Three Bears then went to check upstairs.

"Someone's been sleeping in my bed!" growled Daddy Bear.

"Someone's been sleeping in my bed too!" said Mummy Bear.

"Someone's been sleeping in my bed and, look, she is still there!" said Baby Bear starting to cry.

This woke Goldilocks who was shocked to see the Three Bears standing over her. She quickly jumped out of bed, ran down the stairs and out into the wood. And Goldilocks never came back to the cottage again.

Goldilocks and the Three Bears

One day Goldilocks was walking through the woods when she came to the Three Bears' cottage. When she saw the door was open, she stepped inside but there was nobody home. On the table were three bowls of porridge. First she tasted Daddy Bear's large bowl,

"Ooh, too hot!" she cried. Then she tasted Mummy Bear's bowl and that was too cold. But when she tasted Baby Bear's tiny bowl, it was just right, so she ate it all up.

Goldilocks then wanted to sit down. First she chose the biggest chair which belonged to Daddy Bear but that was too hard. The middle chair was Mummy Bear's but that was too soft. Then she sat in Baby Bear's chair and it was just right. But suddenly there was a great CRASH! And she landed on the floor next to the broken chair.

Goldilocks then took a look around the cottage. Feeling a little tired, she decided to have a lie down upstairs. First she tried the biggest bed where Daddy Bear slept but it was not very comfortable. Then she lay down in Mummy Bear's bed but this seemed too soft. At last she tried Baby Bear's bed and it was just perfect. Soon Goldilocks was fast asleep.

A kind lady led him into a dark kitchen but as she offered him some food, Jack heard a terrifying roar and the whole castle shook.

"Fee, Fi, Fo, Fum, I smell the blood of an Englishman."

"Quick, hide in this cupboard," called the lady just before a huge giant came pounding into the kitchen.

Luckily for Jack, as soon as the giant began to eat, he became calmer. Jack was brave enough to peer out. Never before had he seen such an enormous person.

The giant's wife was a clever lady and played her harp so sweetly that the giant fell asleep. Waiting until she heard him snore, she ran to the cupboard to free Jack.

Thrusting a bag of gold coins into his hand, she told him to flee. Just at that moment the giant woke up and chased Jack down the beanstalk. But as Jack finally reached the ground, he quickly grabbed an axe and chopped the beanstalk down.

Jack's mother ran out when she heard all the noise.

"Look, Mother, we are rich," cried Jack handing her the bag of gold coins.
And from that day, Jack and his mother never went hungry again.

Jack and the Beanstalk

Jack was a lazy boy and never helped his poor mother. One day she asked him to sell their only cow at the market because they had no money for food. But before he reached the market, Jack swapped the cow for a bag of magic beans. When his mother heard this she was very angry. She threw the beans out of the window and sent Jack to bed.

The next morning, to Jack's huge surprise, he found a giant beanstalk outside his window.
"So they were magic beans after all!" he cried.

Wondering how far the beanstalk stretched, Jack climbed and climbed until he reached the top. He was now in a very strange land. He knocked on the door of a huge castle.

But the Three Little Pigs were ready. When the Wolf climbed down the chimney he fell straight into a pot on the fire! He howled as he jumped out and fled into the woods. The Three Little Pigs knew the Big Bad Wolf would not be coming back again!

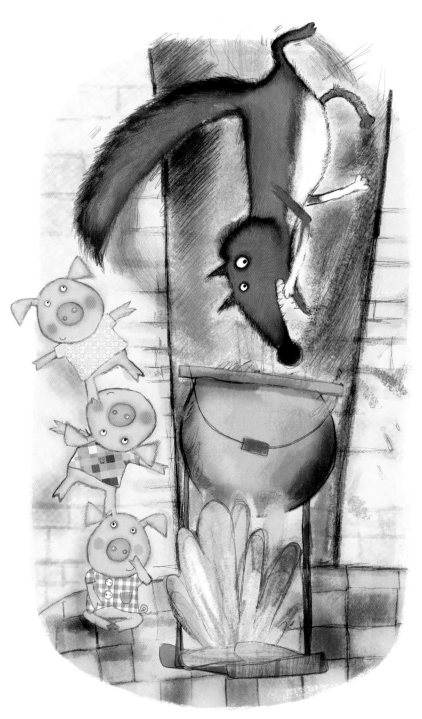

The frightened Little Pig ran to his brother's house which was made of sticks. But the Big Bad Wolf followed. "Little Pigs, Little Pigs, let me in," he cried.

"No, no," squealed the second Little Pig, "Not by the hair on my chinny-chin-chin, I will not let you in!" So the Big Bad Wolf huffed and he puffed and he blew the house of sticks down.

Now the third Little Pig was very clever. He had built his house out of bricks. So all three Little Pigs were cosy and safe inside when they heard the Big Bad Wolf call, "Little Pigs, Little Pigs, let me in!" And when they refused, the Big Bad Wolf huffed and he puffed. But he could not blow the brick house down. And so he climbed on to the roof.

The Three Little Pigs

One day the Three Little Pigs set off to start a new life. Their mother was sad as she waved goodbye but she knew her house was too small for them now. "Beware of the Big Bad Wolf!" she called after them.

Soon they met a man who was selling straw. The first Little Pig bought some and started building his own house. He did not notice that someone was watching him. Just as he had finished there was a knock at the door.

"Little Pig, Little Pig, let me in," cried the Big Bad Wolf. "Not by the hair on my chinny-chin-chin," the Little Pig replied. "Then I'll huff and I'll puff and I'll blow your house down," shouted the Wolf. And he huffed and he puffed and he blew the straw house down.

was dressed in the most beautiful ball gown.

"Now hurry," her fairy godmother told her. "And remember, you must be back by midnight otherwise you will be changed back into your rags."

"I'll remember," smiled Cinderella as she stepped into the carriage.

When she arrived at the palace everyone wanted to know who the beautiful girl was. Even her step-sisters did not recognise her. The prince only had eyes for Cinderella and danced with her all evening. Cinderella was so happy, she forgot her fairy godmother's warning. And at the stroke of midnight she suddenly panicked. As she ran from the prince, she dropped one of her glass slippers.

For weeks the prince searched for Cinderella but nobody knew where she lived. He sent his footmen to find the girl who fitted the glass slipper. When they knocked on the door of Cinderella's house, her step-sisters tried in vain to squeeze their feet into the slipper. They said that no other girl lived with them but when the footmen found Cinderella, the glass slipper fitted perfectly.

Cinderella and her prince were married soon afterwards and lived a very happy life together.

Cinderella

Cinderella lived in a big house with her father, her stepmother and two step-sisters. She loved her father very much and he loved her but when he died, everything changed. Her stepmother and step-sisters were cruel to her. Poor Cinderella had to do all the chores and was made to wear rags.

One day there was huge excitement when an invitation arrived from the palace. The prince was holding a special ball to find his princess. Cinderella's step-sisters could hardly control their excitement.

But when she asked if she could go too, they laughed and said her job was to make them look beautiful.

The night of the ball, Cinderella sat all alone crying in the kitchen. Suddenly there was a bright flash and before her stood a kind and lovely lady who said, "You shall go to the ball!" It was her fairy godmother! Then, to Cinderella's surprise, a beautiful gold carriage appeared with two splendid white horses. "They will take you to the ball," her fairy godmother explained.

"But I have nothing to wear," Cinderella told her sadly. Her fairy godmother smiled and waved her wand. In an instant, Cinderella

"Come in," called a very croaky voice. The room was very dark and Little Red Riding Hood was shocked to see how much Grandma had changed.

"Oh Grandma, what big eyes you have," she whispered.

"All the better to see you with my dear," came the reply.

And when Grandma snatched one of her delicious cakes she gasped, "Oh Grandma, what big hands you have!"

As the greedy wolf gobbled the cake, Little Red Riding Hood shrieked in terror, "Oh Grandma, what big teeth you have!"

"All the better to eat you with my dear," laughed the wolf, leaping out of the bed.

Just at that moment, a woodcutter was passing by the cottage and heard Little Red Riding Hood's screams. As he rushed in, the wolf escaped and limped into the woods. The woodcutter then found poor Grandma in the wardrobe. She was so happy to see that Little Red Riding Hood was safe. After a delicious tea, Little Red Riding Hood ran all the way home and never talked to strangers again.

Little Red Riding Hood

Little Red Riding Hood waved to her mother as she set off to see her grandma. She hurried through the woods, carefully holding on to her basket. She had made Grandma some lovely cakes.

Suddenly a hungry wolf appeared and asked in a friendly voice, "And where are you going?"

"I'm going to visit my sick grandma," replied Little Red Riding Hood. The wolf suggested she should take some flowers to her grandma. And while she stopped to pick the flowers, the wolf raced ahead to Grandma's cottage.

When she reached the cottage, Little Red Riding Hood found the front door was open. She tiptoed in and then headed for Grandma's bedroom and knocked gently.

Toddler

Story Time

Through the Year

spring

summer

autumn

winter

Can you spot the difference in the trees?

Shapes

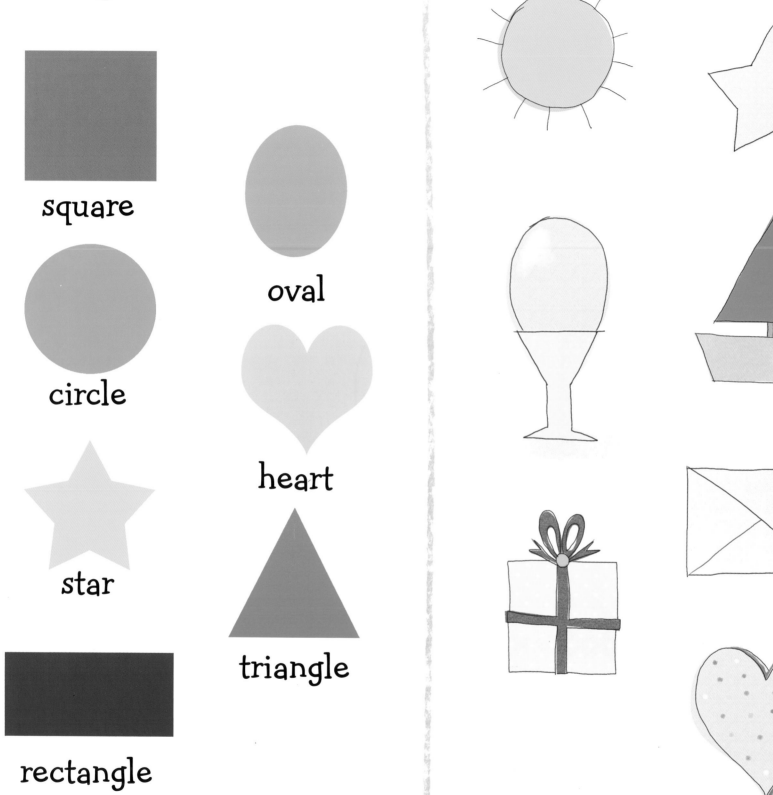

square

circle

star

rectangle

oval

heart

triangle

Can you match the shapes to the objects?

Colours

red

blue

yellow

green

black

orange

pink

brown

purple

Look around your house to see if you can find each colour.

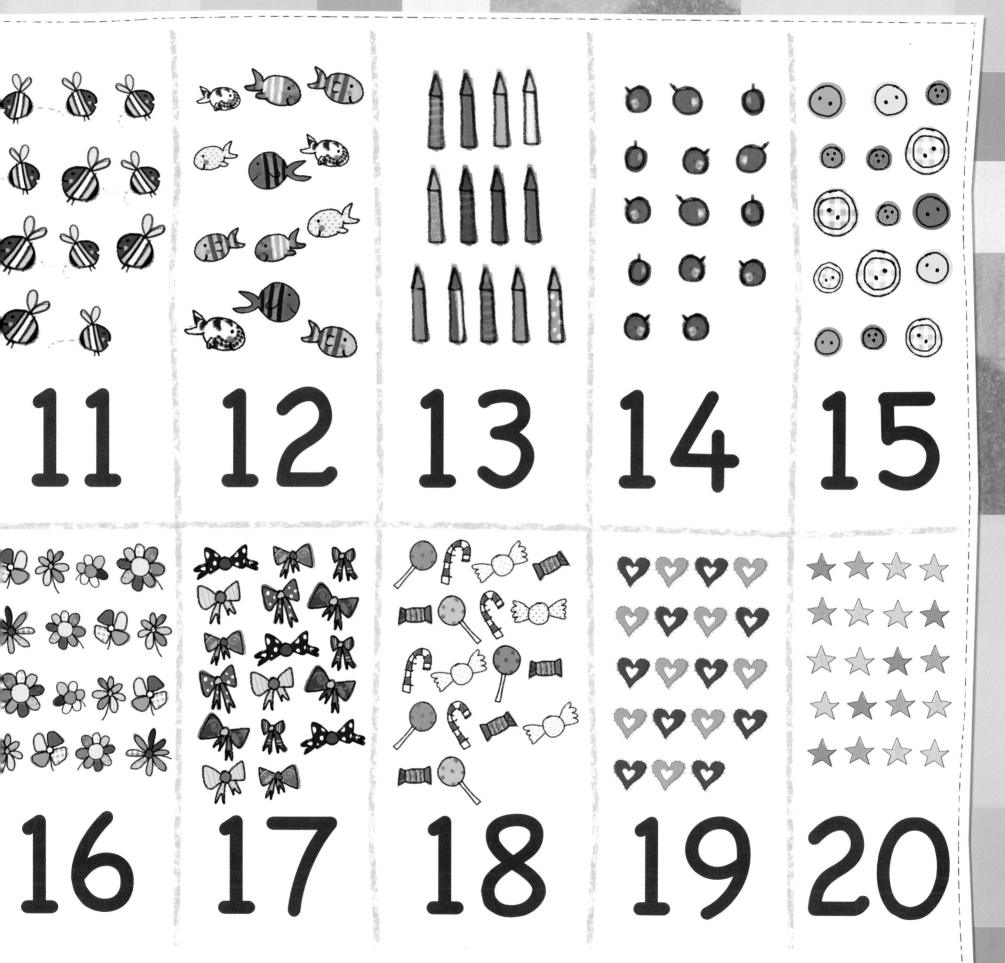

11 12 13 14 15

16 17 18 19 20

How many flowers are there? Now try counting to 20!

Counting to 20

1

2

3

4

5

6

7

8

9

10

How many cats can you see? Now try counting the mice!

o

p

q

r

s

t

u

v

w

x

y

z

Can you find the first letter of your name?

My abc

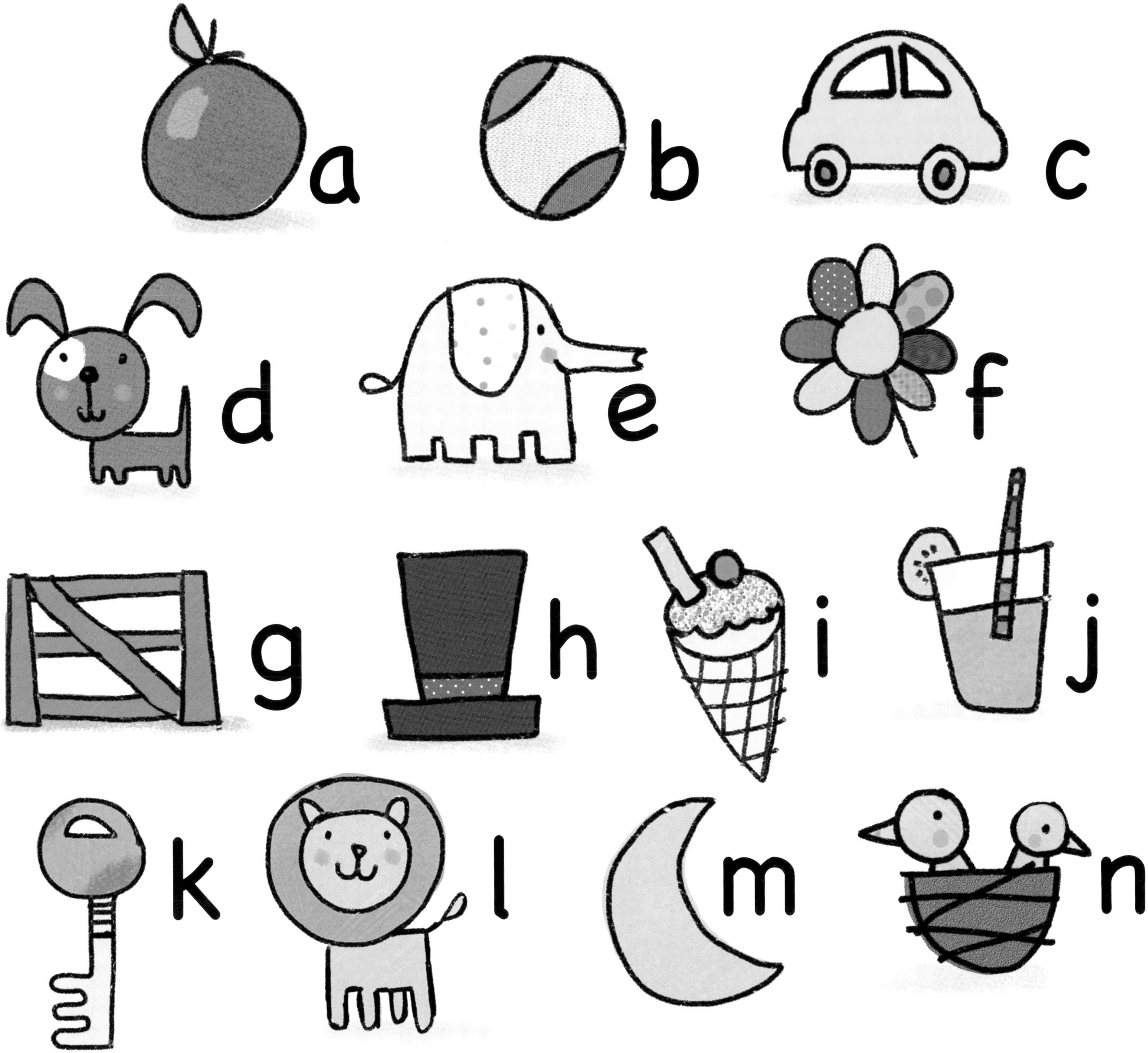

a

b

c

d

e

f

g

h

i

j

k

l

m

n

Can you sing the alphabet?

Toddler
Learning

Party Time

blowing

standing

laughing

clapping

sitting

Who is not wearing a party hat?

At the Seaside

digging

carrying

building

drinking

swimming

How many buckets can you find?

At the Park

sleeping

swinging

sliding

climbing

eating

What do you like doing in the park?

At the Activity Centre

skipping

throwing

jumping

kicking

See if you can jump up and down!

At the Nursery

playing

running

dancing

singing

painting

Which songs do you like to sing?

Toddler
Playtime

In the Country

bird

squirrel

butterfly

rabbit

owl

tree

flowers

mouse

How many animals can you spot?

train

shops

bus

Find the cakes, the shoes and the cat.

In the Town

van

motorbike

scooter

tricycle

car

Can you name the vehicles?

Which fruit do you like best?

At the Supermarket

milk

meat

vegetables

What would you put in your trolley?

Can you make any animal noises?

On the Farm

MOO

MOO

NEIGH

WOOF

How many animals can you name?

Toddler

On The Move

My Pets

dog

rabbit

cat

hamster

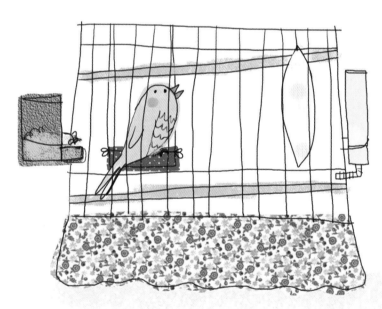

budgie

Can you give each pet a name?

My Toys

zebra

elephant

sword

giraffe

telephone

robot

lion

ball

monkey

bricks

tiara

teddy bear

dinosaur

mask

crocodile

Can you name the wild animals?

My Clothes and Shoes

dress

t-shirt

tights

trousers

coat

jumper

skirt

shoes

shorts

vest

hat

gloves

boots

socks

slippers

Which of these clothes do you have?

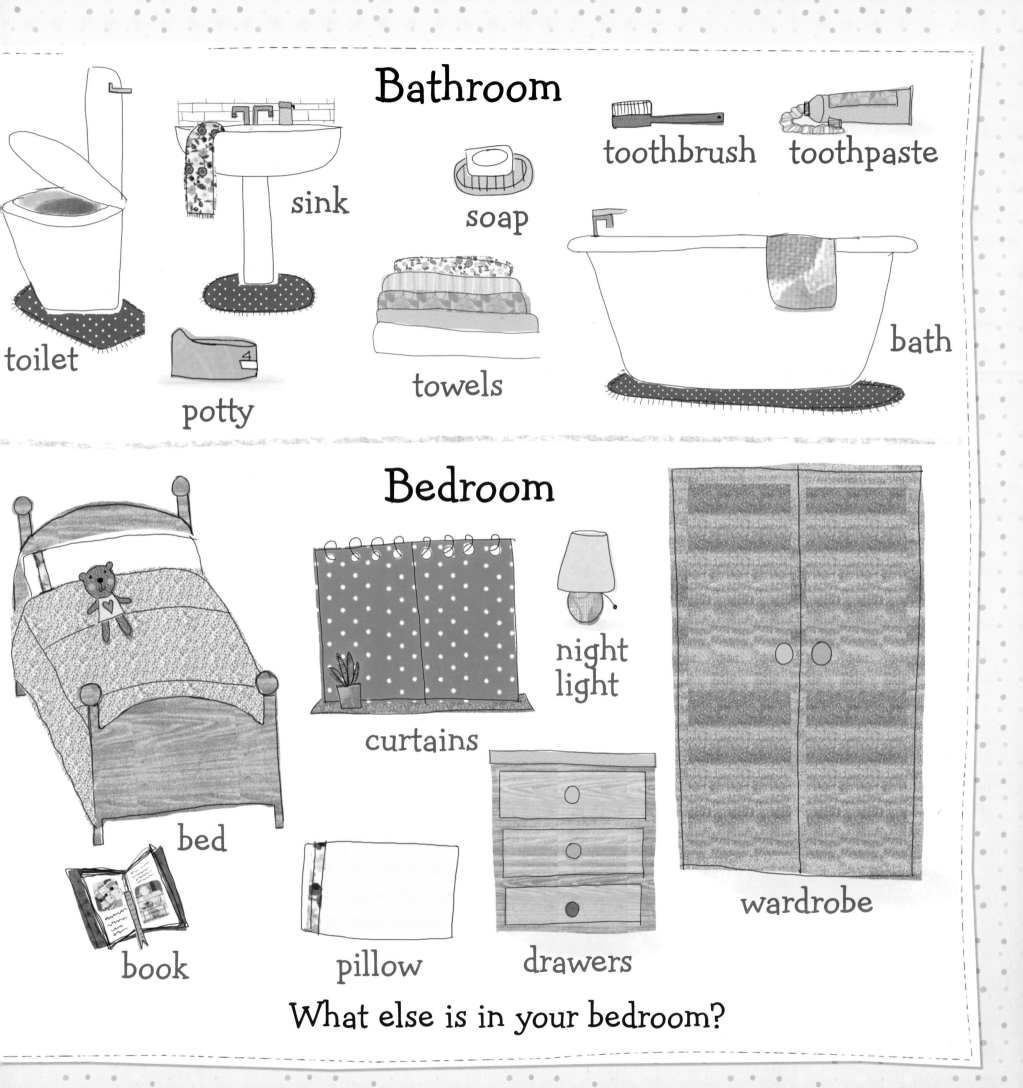

Bathroom

toothbrush

toothpaste

soap

sink

bath

toilet

towels

potty

Bedroom

night
light

curtains

bed

wardrobe

book

pillow

drawers

What else is in your bedroom?

My Home

Living room

table

computer

vase

sofa

television

picture

mirror

chair

window

Kitchen

knife

fork

teapot

plate

cup

washing machine

fridge

Can you point to each picture and say what it is?

Toddler World

Contents

This book belongs to:

E L Y S S A

....

Notes to parents

The **Toddler Treasury** is designed, illustrated and written by parents of toddlers who all understand how it's often difficult to find that special, quiet time together. And that's why the treasury is divided into clear sections reflecting the busy lives of today's toddlers. This is a book to be dipped into at different times depending on the mood of your toddler. Each section offers something entirely different but what makes the collection so unique is the interactive element on every page:

• **Toddler World** provides an opportunity to teach basic vocabulary by looking at familiar images from around the house. Encourage your child to point at every picture and say the word. Then relate the image to the rooms or toys in your house using the questions provided as prompts.

• **Toddler on the Move** captures all the familiar places you and your toddler might visit regularly. This is where you can have lots of fun with making animal noises. Try to make looking at the pictures into a guessing game and this way your toddler will love to show off!

• **Toddler Playtime** introduces lots of 'action words' so there's potential here for encouraging your toddler to mimic some of the actions from the illustrations while also increasing vocabulary.

• **Toddler Learning** gives you all you need to introduce your toddler to the all-important basic concepts of the alphabet, numbers, colours, shapes and nature. Take your time over this section and return to it often but always keep it light-hearted and stop when your toddler is losing interest.

• **Toddler Story Time** has five well-loved fairy tales for you to share so snuggle up and enjoy. Introducing your toddler to stories will have huge learning benefits later so take time to look at the pictures together and try to anticipate what happens next in the story. Also, try to use different voices depending on the characters as your toddler will love to hear you really engaging and is more likely to remember the story.

• **Toddler Quiz** is a game where you can have lots of fun at the same time as reinforcing all your toddler has learnt throughout the treasury. Four separate sections test memory skills with the help of picture clues, so take time over each question and don't try to do the whole quiz in one session. Learning is all about building confidence and the key to success is for you to be encouraging at all times and always give plenty of praise. Remember this is a game, so make sure you are showing that you are enjoying it too!

Bye for now!